There Was an Old Lady Who Swallowed a Fly

ILLUSTRATED BY

GLEN HAY

GT
PUBLISHING

New York

There was an old lady who swallowed a fly.
I don't know why she swallowed the fly.
Perhaps she'll die.

There was an old lady who swallowed a spider
that wiggled and jiggled and tickled inside her.
She swallowed the spider to catch the fly.
I don't know why she swallowed the fly.
Perhaps she'll die.

There was an old lady who swallowed a bird.
How absurd to swallow a bird!
She swallowed the bird to catch the spider
that wiggled and jiggled and tickled inside her.
She swallowed the spider to catch the fly.
I don't know why she swallowed the fly.
Perhaps she'll die.

There was an old lady who swallowed a cat.
Think of that, she swallowed a cat!
She swallowed the cat to catch the bird.
How absurd to swallow a bird!

She swallowed the bird to catch the spider
that wiggled and jiggled and tickled inside her.
She swallowed the spider to catch the fly.
I don't know why she swallowed the fly.
Perhaps she'll die.

There was an old lady who swallowed a dog.
Oh, what a hog to swallow a dog!

She swallowed the dog to catch the cat.
She swallowed the cat to catch the bird.
How absurd to swallow a bird!

She swallowed the bird to catch the spider
that wiggled and jiggled and tickled inside her.

She swallowed the spider to catch the fly.
I don't know why she swallowed the fly.
Perhaps she'll die.

There was an old lady who swallowed a goat,
popped open her throat and swallowed a goat.
She swallowed the goat to catch the dog.
She swallowed the dog to catch the cat.
She swallowed the cat to catch the bird.

She swallowed the bird to catch the spider
that wiggled and jiggled and tickled inside her.
She swallowed the spider to catch the fly.
I don't know why she swallowed the fly.
Perhaps she'll die.

There was an old lady who swallowed a cow,
don't ask me how she swallowed a cow.
She swallowed the cow to catch the goat.
She swallowed the goat to catch the dog.
She swallowed the dog to catch the cat.
She swallowed the cat to catch the bird.

She swallowed the bird to catch the spider
that wiggled and jiggled and tickled inside her.
She swallowed the spider to catch the fly.
I don't know why she swallowed the fly.
Perhaps she'll die.

There was an old lady who swallowed a horse.

She died, of course!